Published by
Beverly's Children's Books
Illustrated by Bex Sutton
Edited by Nay Merrill
Copyright @ 2021 by Beverly King
beverlyschildrensbooks@gmail.com

# REVIEWS

"*Alley Cat Finds a Home* is written by Beverly King with heartfelt sincerity and from the perspective of a lost beautiful orange calico cat, while also detailing the internal concerns a cat may have after being rescued from the wild. It shows us that relatively small actions can have massive impacts on improving the lives of animals in which we share this world with. Great job Beverly!"

- Brad Stokes, City Councilman

"This story captures the joy of the human animal bond and highlights the unconditional love and companionship of our furry friends. Additionally it demonstrates the hard work and dedication of saving animals and the success of rescue and foster programs!"

- Christine Johnson, Doctor of Veterinary Medicine, cVMA

"What a precious book! The story and the illustrations are truly captivating. Beverly's love for animals shines through every page. Truly heartwarming story about a stray cat becoming part of a family. Being an animal lover and animal advocate myself, I love the questions and the educational section at the end. Not to mention the additional bonus of the coloring section, very clever! Excited to share this with the kids in my family!"

-Summer

"The book *Alley Cat Finds a Home* was written with lots of love and a keen knowledge of animal rescue. It's written with such a caring insight into animals' extraordinary love to all of us. I love her care and attention to all of the details in this book that draws you in. This book is a must-have for all animal lovers out there!! The feature at the end to give education on cats to young children, such an excellent section for them to color as well!! Well done, Beverly!"

- Clara

'This book is so much fun to read to my girls—they especially loved the vibrant colors and easy-to-understand storyline! It's also a great story that shows kids how important it is to make animals feel loved and safe. Your beautiful book helped my children understand what it was like for Millie to go from a stray cat to pampered pet!'

- Joanna

"I absolutely love EVERY part of this book! It's very close to my heart having been involved in animal rescue for 10 years. I love how the story is told from the cat's perspective with a happy ending! Which of course is what we all want in animal rescue! The illustrations and story capture trapping, fostering and adopting homeless/stray cats perfectly. I believe that this book will have a large impact on kids to help educate them on kindness & compassion."

- Shannon, Animal Rescuer

# DEDICATION

Thank you to my friends, Lisa Wickard, Joanna Tjadena, Loren Jackson, Felicia Gartung; my sisters-in-law, Cindy King and Kathy Gau; my daughter, Sierra King; and to my mom, Mary Stewart, for their valuable suggestions along the way.

I dedicate this book to The Animal Welfare League of Elmore County, for who I foster for, and to all the people out there that help with and support their local rescues! Because of your help, these animals have a chance to survive and thrive into beautiful, loving family members.

Animal Welfare League of Elmore County, Inc.

501c3 Nonprofit
(208) 921-5532

AnimalWelfareLeagueOfElmore@gmail.com
http://www.awlelmore.org
@AWLElmore

Donation drop off: 1291 N. 14th E. Mountain Home, ID. 86347

# ALLEY CAT
## FINDS A HOME

One day while playing in the alley, I saw two ladies looking for something. They looked in empty boxes, in garbage cans, and over fences.

8

I heard one of them say, "She has to be here. I know I saw her." I wasn't sure who they were talking about. I hadn't seen anyone around for a while.

9

One lady said, "Angel, let's go get some food to set out and come back later." I wondered who the food was for.

Later that day, I woke up from my nap and heard the two ladies again.

One of them said, "Ricki, let's leave the food here in this box, and we'll come back later to check and see if it's been eaten.

After they walked away, I slowly went over to see what they had left behind. It was a bowl of tuna! The tuna smelled so good that I had to try some. It tasted amazing. So amazing that I had to try more and more until it was all gone.

I wasn't sure who it was for, but I hoped they didn't mind that I ate it all up!

Later that night, the ladies came back, and they noticed the tuna was gone. Ricki smiled and said, "I knew she was still here."

Angel said, "Let's leave the rest of the tuna here and come back tomorrow." The smell of the tuna brought me out of hiding, and as I ventured out, I bumped into a box, causing it to make a noise.

They both turned around and saw me. "There she is!" they yelled. I looked around and saw no one. That's when I realized they were talking about me.

13

They had brought the tuna for me. I had never seen them before, but somehow, they knew I was here. The two ladies walked away smiling. Then Angel turned around and said, "We will be back tomorrow."

A warm, loving feeling that I had never felt before came over me. The next day, as the sun came up, the ladies returned with more food and water.

I was so excited to see them! They laid the food and water down and watched me from a distance.

I heard them talking about how pretty I was with my calico colors of orange, brown, and black, along with my big green eyes.

I watched them carefully as I ate the food and drank the fresh water they had brought me.

Each day, they brought me more food and water and sat a little closer to me. Then one day, they reached out to touch me. It startled me, and I moved away.

18

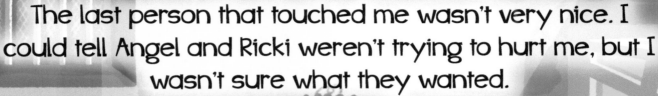

The last person that touched me wasn't very nice. I could tell Angel and Ricki weren't trying to hurt me, but I wasn't sure what they wanted.

As they left that afternoon, they had bigger smiles on their faces than I had seen before.

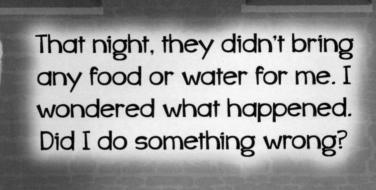

That night, they didn't bring any food or water for me. I wondered what happened. Did I do something wrong?

I felt empty inside, and the warm feeling from before was gone. I waited for them for a long time, but I went to sleep hungry that night and wondered, *Why didn't they come back?*

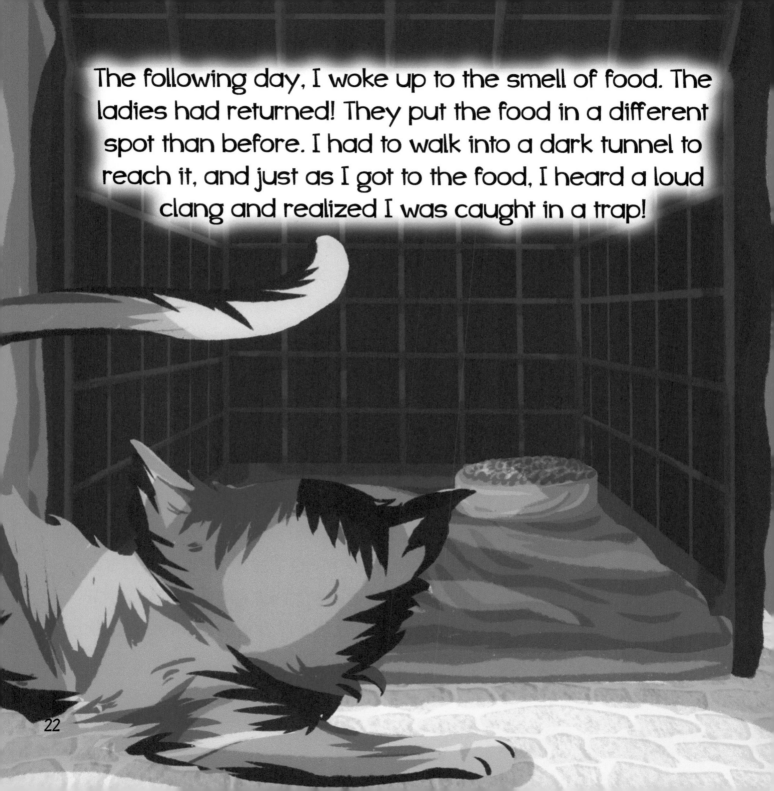

The following day, I woke up to the smell of food. The ladies had returned! They put the food in a different spot than before. I had to walk into a dark tunnel to reach it, and just as I got to the food, I heard a loud clang and realized I was caught in a trap!

22

I was scared and didn't know what was happening. Angel and Ricki picked up the trap, and Angel said, "I am so happy we got her. Now we can get her checked out by our veterinarian and make sure she is healthy."

I didn't know what a veterinarian was, but they took me to a place that had a funny smell. A man named Dr. Sunil looked me over.

He checked my fur and looked in my eyes, my ears, and my mouth.

Then he poked me with a sharp needle. He said I was very healthy for living in the alley. Then he placed me in a cat carrier.

Angel and Ricki then took me to a big room with lots of toys and food. There was another cat in the room as well. She was my size and pure black with green eyes.

Ricki took me out of the carrier and put me on the floor. I was scared and had no idea where I was. I saw a box that looked familiar from the alley, so I went and hid inside of it.

LITTER BOX

I heard Angel and Ricki talking to someone they called Bob. They told him where I was caught and what the veterinarian had said. Sometime later, Bob came to the room's glass door that I was in and watched the other cat and me.

I wasn't sure about that other cat, and she wasn't sure about me. We hissed at each other and stayed apart on opposite sides of the room.

The following day, Bob brought us fresh food and water and cleaned the litter boxes we filled during the night.

30

Later in the day, Bob noticed that the other cat and I were still not friends, but we were no longer hissing at each other.

LITTER BOX

02:27

I was Millie, and she was Lilly. Bob spent lots of time with us, taking pictures and videos as we played with the toys.

Over the next few days, the other cat and I became friends, and Bob started calling us Millie and Lilly.

Bob held us and talked to us with a soft voice, saying, "You are safe, and we will find you a forever home soon."

A couple of days later, Bob told us that a family had seen the pictures and videos and wanted to meet us.

The family came by to see Lilly and me later that day. There was a small boy with a baseball cap called Max and a small curly-haired girl they called Maxine.

34

They picked us up and held us in their arms close to their bodies, and suddenly, we both felt that warm feeling inside once again.

We started purring as they petted our fur and scratched our heads while their parents filled out the adoption paperwork that Bob had handed them.

Then Max and Maxine told their mom and dad that we were perfect!

LITTER BOX

35

Once we arrived at our new home, Max carried us into a room and took us out of our carriers.

The floor was soft and cozy compared to the cold, hard floor we were used to. Max and Maxine showed us around, letting us know where to find our food, water, and litter box.

They played with us for a while and then let us rest. We snuggled up in one of the beds they got for us and went right to sleep, tired from all the excitement of the day.

The following day, Max and Maxine left the door open to the room we were in to explore the rest of the house. We had so much space to run and jump!

I had lots of room to run and jump in the alley, but it was better here. I felt alone and sad in the alley. In this space, I felt warm and happy.

I thought life was supposed to be rough since living in the alley was all I knew. I had no idea living with a loving family would be so amazing.

Lilly and I played for a long time.

We ran up and down the hallways, jumped on everything we could find, and chased all the toys that Max and Maxine threw for us.

After a while, we were tired, so we found a fluffy bed, snuggled up together, and fell fast asleep.

The following day, Bob came for a visit and watched how we played. He looked happy as he watched us.

He held us both one last time to let us know that his job was now complete and it was time to help the next cats in need.

We purred as he held us, and he let us know that we were now home, home to stay.

41

42

44

45

# QUESTIONS:

1. Why should you spay or neuter your cat?

2. How many litters can a cat have in its lifetime?

3. At what age can a cat have kittens?

4. Why should you be cautious when handling a stray animal?

5. Have you ever thought about helping with any rescue groups?

6. Have you ever stopped to help an animal in need?

# GLOSSARY:

## Making biscuits:

Cat kneading, also known as "making biscuits," is considered a cat trait inherited from your domesticated feline's wild ancestors. While your cat may look as though they are kneading dough, in the wild, this is their way of making a nest and checking for any potential predators or dangerous things lurking beneath their spot of choice.

## Marking territory:

Territorial behaviors and a need to demonstrate to others where their territory lies are common across all cats. Your pet cat and wild cats will usually do the following to mark their territory: spraying, rubbing their face (because of the multiple scent glands on their heads), and scratching (because of the scent glands located in their paws).

## Grooming:

A shared cat characteristic is that wild and domesticated cats spend between 30-50% of their time grooming. This is essential for hunting as it helps keep their scent neutral to stay undetected by their chosen prey.

## Hunting:

Your cat's hunting instincts are incredibly similar to that of a big cat. The ambush technique and waiting and pouncing on their prey are the same amongst all big cats. And they even share similar hunting patterns, choosing to pursue at dusk and dawn mainly. Some people believe barn cats do not need to be fed and that all they need to survive is the prey they catch. That is incorrect—barn cats need to be provided with the required protein for the energy it takes to be great hunters. A well-fed cat makes a great addition to any barn.

## Sleep:

Cats conserve energy by sleeping more than most animals, especially as they grow older. The daily sleep duration varies between 12 and 16 hours, with 13 and 14 hours being the average. Some cats can sleep as much as 20 hours. The term "cat nap" for a short rest refers to the cat's tendency to fall asleep (lightly) for a brief period.

## Vision:

Cats have excellent night vision, which enables them to hunt at night. While cats can't see in total darkness, they can see much better in dim light than we can.

49

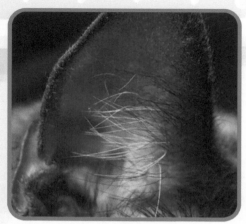

## Hearing:

A cat's ears are very sensitive and can hear a wide range of sounds, including high frequency (ultrasonic), that humans cannot hear. A cat will usually turn its head to the direction of the sound, which helps both visually and with hearing.

## Smell:

Cats have a very acute sense of smell that helps locate prey or danger (for our indoor cats: unfamiliar animals, people, or changes in their environment).

## Taste:

Cats live up to their reputation as "finicky" eaters, which prevents them from eating something that might be toxic in the wild. The rough surface of the tongue contains taste buds and also helps remove dirt from the fur. When you have two companion cats, you will often notice one grooming the other on the hard-to-reach spots.

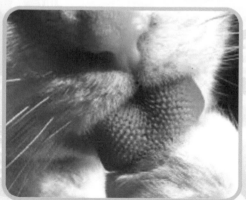

## Touch:

A cat's whiskers are very sensitive to the slightest touch. Whiskers are used for monitoring the environment and are used in a friendly greeting with another cat. The cat has four rows of whiskers on the upper lip on each side. Smaller whiskers can be found on other body parts, including above each eye, on the cheeks, and the backs of the front paws. You will note that a cat sheds whiskers as it does its fur, but whiskers should never be cut as this alters the cat's ability to orient itself.

# AUTHOR
# BEVERLY KING

Beverly King was raised on a small family farm and was taught to respect and care for animals at a young age. She shares her love of animals with everyone around. She and her mom have been running a successful animal boarding business for over twenty years and have enjoyed working with each family member, big or small, who have come in to stay for short or long visits over the years. She continues to help as many animals as possible, and with each sale of this book, she will give the proceeds as a donation to animal rescues.

# ILLUSTRATOR BEX SUTTON

Bex Sutton is a UK-based illustrator who works on a variety of projects. With the company of her husband, two cats, and giant puppy, she can be found illustrating day and night on her computer, losing herself in a new magical world she designs. She can be reached by email at bex@primalst.com

LITTER BOX

Lightning Source UK Ltd.
Milton Keynes UK
UKHW050842061021
391741UK00002B/20